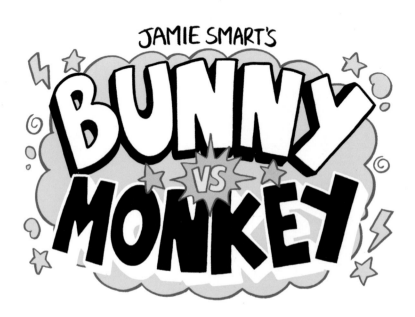

JAMIE SMART'S

BUNNY VS MONKEY

FICKLING
d b
David Fickling Books

THE PHOENIX

Dedicated to everyone who helped to bring this book together.

The comics in this book were originally published as
Bunny vs Monkey: Let the Mayhem Begin! and Bunny vs Monkey: Journey to the Centre of the Eurg-th!

Adaptation design by Laura Bentley, additional artwork and colours by Sammy Borras.
Cover and interior design by Paul Duffield.

Bunny vs Monkey
is A DAVID FICKLING BOOK

First published in Great Britain in 2020 by
David Fickling Books,
31 Beaumont Street,
Oxford, OX1 2NP

Text and illustrations © Fumboo Ltd, 2020

978-1-78845-177-2
13 15 17 19 20 18 16 14

David Fickling Books reg. no. 8340307

A CIP catalogue record for this book
is available from the British Library.

Printed and bound in China by Toppan Leefung.

MIX
Paper from
responsible sources
FSC® C104723

Papers used by David Fickling Books are from
well-managed forests and other responsible sources.

"PROLOGUE!"

AS WINTER CLOSES IN, AND ALL THE WOODLAND ANIMALS LOOK FOR A WARM PLACE TO SLEEP, ONE LONE WHITE BUNNY IS LOOKING FOR HIS FRIENDS.

WEENIE?

PIG?

HEY, BUNNY!

HEYYYY!

WE FOUND A LION!

A LION? ARE YOU... THAT'S A **BEAR**!

SHRIEK!

OH. IS IT NOT THE SAME THING?

HE IS SLEEPY.

5

7

11

ALL THAT LOT WANT TO DO IS MESS ABOUT IN THE WOODS, PLAYING GAMES.

HOWEVER I, **SKUNKY,** HAVE AN INCREDIBLE MIND, AND I REFUSE TO LET IT GO TO WASTE.

SO I BUILT MYSELF THIS UNDERGROUND LAIR...

...WHERE I INVENT **THE MOST REMARKABLE CREATIONS IN THE WORLD!!**

GASP- SKUNKY, THIS IS IMPRESSIVE! I COULD USE THESE MACHINES TO RULE THE WOODS!

I <u>KNEW</u> YOU WOULD APPRECIATE MY GENIUS.

IN FACT, I HAVE ALREADY CONSTRUCTED THE PERFECT DEVICE FOR YOUR NUTBAR SCHEMES.

WANNA SEE! WANNA SEE!

I TAKE MOST OF MY INSPIRATION FROM ANIMALS THEMSELVES. FOR T<u>HI</u>S INVENTION, I LOOKED TO THE MOST TERRIFYING BEAST OF ALL..

SHOOF!

GASP!

18

23

27

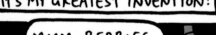

"CLOWNING AROUND!"

THESE WOODS USED TO BE PEACEFUL, BUT NOW ALL ANYONE DOES IS FIGHT!

WE SHOULD TRY TO CHEER EVERYONE UP!

CLONK!

ARGH!

LET'S HIDE A STICK AND EVERYONE HAS TO FIND IT!

WE COULD HIDE IT IN A PILE OF STICKS.

OR, WE COULD PUT ON A **CIRCUS**!

WELL, I SUPPOSE.

AND EVERY GOOD CIRCUS NEEDS... CLOWNS!

WE COULD DRESS UP LIKE CLOWNS!

LET'S GO!

SCAMPER!

A FEW MINUTES LATER...

HEE HEE!

HEE!

READY?

READY, GO!

SHRIEK!! SHRIIIIEK!

34

I COMPLETELY FORGOT HOW **SCARY** CLOWNS ARE!

WELL WE CAN'T CANCEL THE CIRCUS NOW, I'VE ALREADY DRAWN A FACE ON A BALLOON!

THEN THE SHOW MUST GO ON! BUT WE PROMISE NOT TO LOOK AT EACH OTHER!

DEAL.

CIRKUZ

ROLL UP, ROLL UP, TO OUR **SPECIAL CIRCUS!** SEE THE UPSETTING CLOWNS!

HMM, I SUPPOSE I COULD TAKE A BREAK.

BUDGE OVER! I WANT TO SIT AT THE FRONT!

HOI!

FIRST UP, MEET OUR CLOWN...

I CAN'T LOOK...

...IT'S **BONKY PIG-O!**

TAA DAA.

36

"ACTION BEAVER"

DOWN BY THE RIVER, POOR PIG WAS JUST TRYING TO EAT HIS PUDDING IN PEACE...

SOAR!!

HAR HAR! GIMME YOUR PUD, PUDGY! I AM A DELICATE AND GRACEFUL BUTTERFLY!

CRUMP!

ARGH! HOW D'YOU FLY THESE THINGS?

SKUNKY, I'M TIRED OF YOUR INVENTIONS. THEY EITHER BREAK, GO MAD, BLOW UP OR SLAM ME INTO THE GROUND.

I'M STARTING TO THINK THEY'RE BAD IDEAS.

HOW DARE YOU! MY CREATIONS ARE EXQUISITE...INGENIOUS. THEY'RE GOING WRONG BECAUSE I'M GIVING THEM TO A MONKEY.

WELL, MAYBE WE SHOULD HIRE SOMEONE TO TEST THEM FIRST!

HMM, WELL, I DO KNOW SOMEONE. A STUNTMAN OF SORTS. BUT HE'S A LOOSE CANNON, A MAVERICK. ADDICTED TO DANGER!

SOUNDS PERFECT!

38

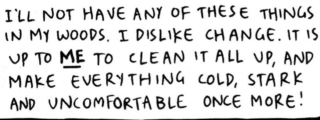

45

"BONJOUR, LE FOX"

47

48

53

NEXT MORNING...

HEY! DUMB BUNNY, AND YOUR DUMB FRIENDS!

YOU'RE DUMB!

WELL NOW, THAT'S JUST BAD TIMING. SINCE PIG AND WEENIE HAVE JUST GLUED THEIR HEADS TOGETHER, YOU HAVE A POINT.

RRG!

HEE HEE!

OH, WELL, SORRY. IT WAS MORE INTENDED AS A GENERAL INSULT.

ANYWAY! I'M HERE TO SMASH UP YOUR LITTLE CORNER OF THE WOODS, AND DRIVE YOU ALL AWAY!

HAR HAR!

I'D LIKE TO SEE YOU TRY!

ME, TOO! SKUNKY SHOULD BE HERE BY NOW!

TAA-DAA! I HAVE INVENTED MY GREATEST WEAPON YET!

OH, THANK GOODNESS.

IT WILL STRIKE FEAR INTO YOUR HEARTS, AND UNWELCOME NERVOUS GURGLES INTO YOUR BELLIES. IT IS THE DESTROYER OF WORLDS, THE CRUSHER OF DREAMS...

57

64

65

GRUUUUU!! THERE IS NO MONKEY HERE, JUST ME...

...CATER-PILLAR-ZILLA!

SCREEEAM!

IT **IS** ME, REALLY. THIS IS SKUNKY'S LATEST INVENTION, AND IT MADE YOU SCREAM LIKE A BABY!

RESULT!

NOW, IF YOU'LL EXCUSE US, WE'RE BUSY CONSUMING EVERY LAST TRACE OF NATURE.

WHAT... WHAT **IS** THAT THING?

THE CATERPILLARZILLA CAN CHEW ITS WAY THROUGH FIVE TONNES OF LEAVES IN JUST TEN MINUTES!

CHOMP CHOMP CHOMP

WE'LL HAVE THESE WOODS CHOMPED UP IN NO TIME!

YOU CAN'T DO THIS! GET OUT OF THERE RIGHT NOW, YOU BUNCH OF TROUBLEMAKERS!

CLONK!

THE WHUPPABALOO

I'M PRETTY SURE IT'S THIS WAY.

WHEN DO WE GET TO SIT DOWN? MY MONKEY FEET ARE TIRED!

BUT WE'VE ONLY BEEN WALKING FOR FIVE MINUTES.

YEAH, WELL, MY TOOTSIES ARE MORE PRECIOUS THAN YOURS.

TENDER KISS

I CAN'T EVEN REMEMBER WHAT WE'RE DOING UP HERE.

WE'RE HUNTING THE FEARSOME **WHUPPABALOO**, THE MOST DANGEROUS LIVING THING ON EARTH!

IT'S MYSTERIOUS, LEGENDARY, AND INCREDIBLY HARD TO FIND!

WELL, IT **DOES** SOUND LIKE A LOT OF FUN. THINK OF THE TROUBLE WE COULD CAUSE WITH IT.

EXACTLY! WHICH IS WHY WE NEED TO GET MOVING.

WHERE DID YOU GET YOUR MAP FROM?

I DREW IT MYSELF.

SO IT **MUST** BE RIGHT.

69

73

74

76

"FISH OFF!"

A PEACEFUL MORNING IN THE WOODS...

THAT IS, UNTIL...

... MONKEY TURNS UP!

LOOK, I FOUND A **HORN!**

HONKKKKKK!!

HONKKK!

ZZZ!

WHAT **ARE** YOU DOING?

I AM **FISHING**. I NEVER CATCH ANYTHING, BUT THAT'S HOW I LIKE IT. I JUST FIND IT RELAXING.

SOUNDS **BORING**. I BET I COULD CATCH SOME FISH. CATCH THEM RIGHT UP.

NONSENSE, IT'S AN ART. YOU'D HAVE NO CHANCE.

PAH! GIVE ME THAT ROD, I'LL SHOW YOU HOW TO DO IT.

SNATCH!

79

"MOLE-A-ROLLA!"

It's Saturday morning, and the woodland animals are playing 'CAKE-BALL'.

YOU HIT IT!

HIT WHAT?

I'LL CATCH IT!

(The rules of which, no one's quite sure of...)

FLUMP!

LE FOX, WHAT'S THIS BIG HOLE DOING HERE?

YOU NOTICED IT TOO, HUH?

86

WOULD YOU HAPPEN TO KNOW WHERE I COULD FIND THE OWNER OF THIS FINE WOODLAND?

PERCHANCE?

ARE YOU A WIZARD?

ME? NO SIR, MY NAME IS THEODORE P. WHIBBLEBUSS.

AND I AM A VERY RICH OIL PROSPECTOR.

SHHH!

WHY ARE WE WHISPERING?

WE MADE FIZZY POP ANGRY.

WE DIDN'T MEAN TO!

SHH!

SHH!

FURTHER INTO THE WOODS...

EXCUSE ME, ARE YOU MISTER 'BUNNY'? I FOUND THESE TWO AND THEY WON'T STOP CRYING AND SHUSHING EACH OTHER.

BOO HOO SHH SHH

MONKEY! WHAT DID YOU DO TO THEM?

MONKEY? WHY, MY NAME IS THEODORE P. WHIBBLEBUSS.

SNIFF

91

"QUIET DAY!"

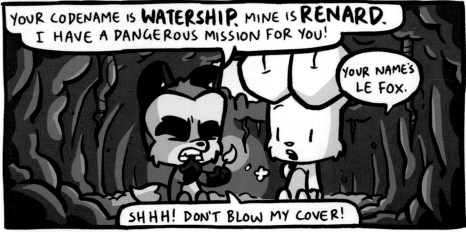

94

95

96

"BRING HIM BACK!"

A BEAUTIFUL EARLY MORNING IN THE WOODS, AND ONE CREATURE IS UP AND ABOUT ALREADY...

FSHOOM!! TING TING! WHUPPP!

...BUT WHERE IS HE OFF TO IN SUCH A HURRY?

HALF AN HOUR EARLIER...

ACTION BEAVER, WE NEED YOU TO STOP PUTTING YOUR HEAD IN THINGS FOR JUST A MOMENT.

SKUNKY HAS A VERY IMPORTANT MISSION FOR YOU.

THIS IS YOUR MISSION, SHOULD YOU ACCEPT IT. METAL STEVE, DANGEROUS CROCODILE ROBOT, HAS STORMED OFF IN A HUFF.

HUFF

101

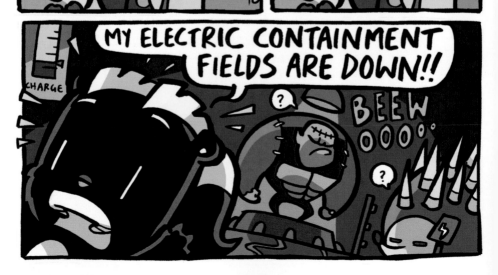

THIS ISN'T _FUN_, MONKEY. THESE ARE DANGEROUS MONSTERS, HELL-BENT ON CRUSHING ALL IN THEIR PATH.

THAT INCLUDES _US_!!

WELL, POTATO POTARTO, I STILL DON'T SEE HOW THIS DAY COULD GET ANY BETTER.

GRUARGHHHH!

OH, WAIT. IT DID.

THE **BEAR!** ALL THIS NOISE MUST HAVE WOKEN HIM FROM HIS HIBERNATION.

I LIKE HIS HAT.

IT'S CLASSY.

SWIPE!

GRAB!

BE CAREFUL, MONKEY! HE'S A GRUMPY WILD ANIMAL!

GIBBER GIBBER GIBBER!

WAIT FOR ME, PIG! WAIT FOR MEEE!

WELL, NO-ONE EVER SAID IT WAS A GRACEFUL NIGHTMARE CREATURE.

CHOMP CHOMP CHOMP

THE NEXT MORNING... WE CAN'T HAVE THAT 'BAT' TERRORISING OUR WOODS!

IT'S TIME WE PUT OUR DIFFERENCES TO ONE SIDE AND TEAMED UP!

YAWN. DO WHAT YOU WANT, I'M GOING BACK TO BED.

FINE, MONKEY. YOU'D PROBABLY RUIN EVERYTHING ANYWAY.

I PROBABLY WOULD.

SKUNKY! YOU KNOW A LOT ABOUT ANIMALS, DO YOU HAVE ANYTHING THAT COULD HELP US?

WHAT, LIKE A BOOK ON BATS? WELL, I DO JUST HAPPEN TO...

THIS IS BRILLIANT! BY LEARNING ABOUT OUR ENEMY, WE CAN DEFEAT HIM.

DEFEAT WHO?

I DON'T REMEMBER, I WAS THINKING ABOUT CUSTARD TARTS.

BATS! BATS!

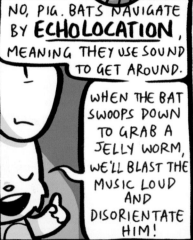

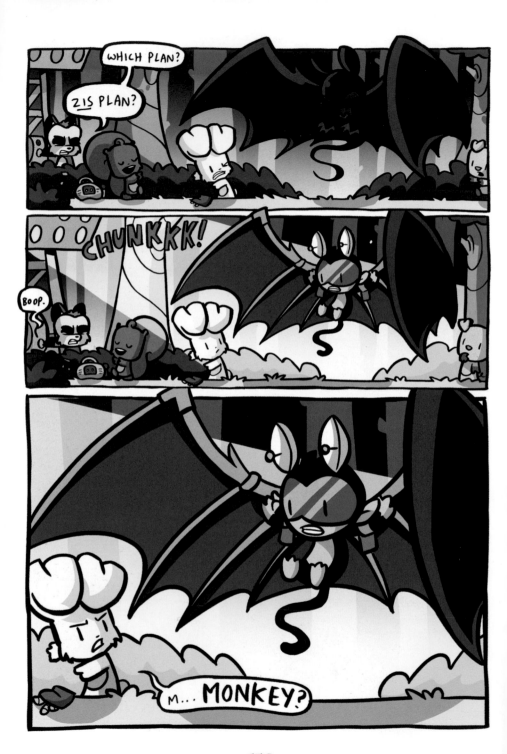

...THE MONKEY!

THOSE AREN'T YOUR ARMS!

THEY ARE! THEY'VE ALWAYS BEEN LIKE THIS.

THEY'RE FAKE! FAKE ARMS!

NOT JUST 'FAKE ARMS', THEY'RE TOP SPEC **ROBOTIC ARM ENHANCERS**, DESIGNED TO BOOST STRENGTH BY 200%.

PROUD!

THEY'RE MY ARMS, OKAY? NOW LET'S FIGHT!!

WELL, IF YOU'RE ALLOWED TO CHEAT, THEN SO AM I.

PIG! GO AND DRESS UP LIKE A WRESTLER, WE'RE TAG-TEAMING!

OKEE DOKEE!

I'M HERE! **RAHHHH!!**

THAT'S NOT A WRESTLER OUTFIT!

WRESTLER? I THOUGHT YOU SAID PLUMBER.

BUT... THAT'S NOT A PLUMBER OUTFIT, EITHER.

117

MY HEAD IS STUCK IN A BUCKET!

YOU NEED **BUTTER** TO GREASE IT OFF!

THE CHEF DEFIES THE RULES, AND STAYS IN THE MATCH!

OI! STUPID BUNNY! ALL THIS MESSING ABOUT, AND WE HAVEN'T ACTUALLY DONE ANY FIGHTING!

I HAVE ONE MORE TEAM MEMBER. UMM...LE FOX?

YOUR ANNOYING LITTLE RODENT INTERRUPTED MY NAP.

ZZNGG!

LE FOX, JOIN MY TEAM! I NEED YOU!

UMM.

NO.

HA **HA**! WELL THAT LEAVES **ME** WITH ONE MORE TEAM MEMBER.

118

125

"THE WISH CANNON"

DEEP UNDERGROUND, IN SKUNKY'S SECRET LAIR...

Y'KNOW, SKUNKY, IT'S STRANGE. EVERY DAY I COME DOWN HERE AND SAY "QUICK, SKUNKY, I NEED AN INVENTION FOR A SPECIFIC TASK!" AND EVERY TIME, YOU JUST HAPPEN TO HAVE BEEN WORKING ON JUST THE RIGHT THING.

YOU MEAN, IT'S ALL A LITTLE TOO CONVENIENT? AS IF IT'S ALL TOO EASY?

WELL, DON'T WORRY ABOUT THAT NOW. HAVE A GO ON MY NEWEST INVENTION, THE WISH CANNON INSTEAD!

OOOH!

THE WISH CANNON SYNTHETICALLY BONDS WITH THE DNA OF WHOEVER IS HOLDING IT, AND INTERPRETS THEIR BRAIN WAVES INTO OBJECTS, WHICH IT THEN PROPELS AT HIGH SPEED!

BASICALLY, IT FIRES WHATEVER YOU WANT!

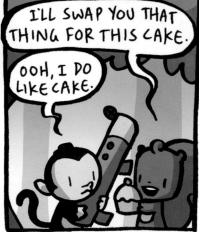

127

128

STAND BACK, SKUNKY! I'M THINKING ABOUT SOME PARTICULARLY MOULDY SANDWICHES!

PAH! THINK YOU CAN DEFEAT ME WITH MY OWN INVENTION?

WHEN I HAVE THE **WISH CANNON DEFLECTOR SHIELD?**

(WHICH I JUST INVENTED.)

THE WHAT?

THE WISH CANNON DEFLECTOR SHIELD, WHEN FIRED AT, DEFLECTS THE SHOT AND TURNS ANYONE NEARBY **INTO THAT WISH!**

WAIT, HANG ON. I'M GETTING CONFUSED WITH THIS NOW.

PYEW!

OH, YOU WERE JUST THINKING OF A STUPID PIG, AND NOW THERE IS ONE!

HUH?

WHAT? I DIDN'T!

PYEW! A HA! THINKING ABOUT A SQUIRREL BEING ATTACKED BY KITTENS, EH? WELL, I DEFLECTED IT!

YOU'RE MAKING THIS UP AS YOU GO ALONG!

"OCTO-BLIVION"

"JOURNEY TO THE CENTRE OF THE EURG-TH"

IT'S A BLISTERINGLY HOT DAY IN THE WOODS, AND ONE INHABITANT ISN'T ENJOYING IT...

MY SNOWMAN MELTED!!

A SNOWMAN? BUT IT HASN'T SNOWED FOR MONTHS... OH.

I MADE HIM OUT OF **CUSTARD.**

TECHNICALLY, HE'S A CUSTARD MAN.

SOB! GOODBYE, OLD FRIEND.

POOEY! SOMETHING SMELLS LIKE RANCID CUSTARD.

BOO HOO!

THIS HEAT IS MAKING LIFE VERY DIFFICULT FOR ALL OF US. LET'S JUST HOPE IT COOLS DOWN SOON.

139

142

"KING PIG!!"

It's Thursday, and Weenie and Pig are being creative...

HEE HEE! I AM DRAWING AN ASTRONAUT GIVING AN ALIEN A KISS!

WHAT HAVE YOU DRAWN, PIG?

I HAVE DRAWN A **CROWN**. PARTLY BECAUSE I ONLY HAVE A YELLOW CRAYON.

I STUFFED ALL THE OTHERS UP MY NOSE.

GASP! IF YOU HAVE A CROWN, YOU KNOW WHAT THAT MEANS!

YES!

WAIT, NO.

146

148

150

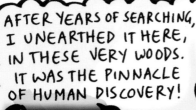

AFTER YEARS OF SEARCHING, I UNEARTHED IT HERE, IN THESE VERY WOODS. IT WAS THE PINNACLE OF HUMAN DISCOVERY!

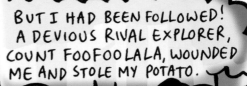

BUT I HAD BEEN FOLLOWED! A DEVIOUS RIVAL EXPLORER, COUNT FOOFOOLALA, WOUNDED ME AND STOLE MY POTATO.

HE CLAIMED ALL MY GLORY. I REMAINED HERE, TOO WEAK TO RETURN HOME.

SO NOW NEITHER OF US CAN ENJOY THE POTATO.

I'M STILL GOING TO EAT THEM OFF THE FLOOR.

HOW DARE YOU.

HEE HEE, LOOK, MISTER FOX! BUNNY TIED A BALLOON AROUND ME SO I WOULDN'T KEEP GETTING LOST.

THE BALLOON.

I REMEMBER IT WELL.

154

SO, YOU THINK IT AMUSING TO REMIND ME OF ALL THIS?
HOW D...
OH, HE'S GONE.
HEY, SO, LE FOX.
I'VE BEEN WATCHING YOU WALKING AROUND, EXPLAINING HOW YOU CAME TO BE IN THE WOODS.
AND YOU KNOW, IT'S WEIRD. I'M SURE YOUR STORY IS DIFFERENT EVERY TIME.
AH, WELL, YOU OF ALL SHOULD RECOGNISE THE TRUTH.
I LIVE HERE AS A GUARDIAN, FORETOLD IN PROPHECY TO GUARD AND PROTECT THE WOODS.
HA! FROM WHAT?
JAMIE

FROM THE TERRIFYING SECRETS THEY HOLD BENEATH. THE DEMONS AND BEASTS OF MAN AND MACHINE, THE NIGHTMARES FOOLISHLY IGNORED, SOON TO RISE AGAIN.

THAT'S NOT VERY FUNNY. EVERYONE ELSE GOT FUNNY STORIES.

ALL STORIES COME FROM TRUTH, SKUNKY.

IT IS UP TO YOU WHICH ONE YOU BELIEVE.

WANT SOME CHIPS? THEY'RE A BIT SOIL-Y.

OOH! CHIPS!

SCREECH!

A SALAD SANDWICH! THAT LOOKS TASTY, CAN I HAVE SOME? SAVES YOU EATING IT.

MEEP!

ARE YOU MY CONSCIENCE?

NO, SILLY! I'M A HAMSTER! HAMSTERS EAT SALAD!

ROLL...BONK!

MMM, SALAD.

IT WON'T GO THROUGH YOUR FORRRCE-FIELD!

AWW, MEEP!

PUFF...HI THERE! I'M BUNNY, WELCOME TO OUR WOODS!

SQUELCH!

I'M PIPI! I'VE BEEN RUNNING AND RUNNING AND RUNNING FOR SO LONG, I'M NOT EVEN SURE WHERE I AM!

I SURE LOVE RUNNING.

MEEP!

WELL, YOU'RE WELCOME TO STAY HERE, WITH US, IF YOU LIKE.

OH, I CAN'T DO THAT. THEY'RE COMING!

MEEP!

WHO ARE?

158

159

160

161

"BEE-DAY!"

BUZZ BUZZ!

BUZZ OOMPH!

BUZZ BUZZ!!

WHAT'S WRONG WITH YOU ALL? STOP IT!

BUT IT'S **BEE-DAY**, MISTER MONKEY!

BIDET?

BEE-DAY IS WHEN WE ALL DRESS UP LIKE FUNNY FUZZY BEES, AND CELEBRATE BEES BECAUSE BEES MAKE HONEY.

BECAUSE HONEY IS YUMMY!

WELL, YOU'RE ALL STILL STUPID. VERY WELL DONE. I REFUSE TO BE INVOLVED IN YOUR SILLY BEE-DAY.

OKEE DOKEE! BUZZZZ! HEE HEE!

I CHANGED MY MIND! AND I BROUGHT SOME GUESTS OF HONOUR!

I STOLE THEM OFF A TREE.

A BEE HIVE!

164

165

169

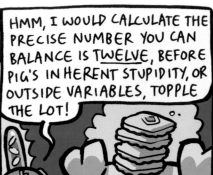

170

171

175

176

177

"I, ROBOT CROCODILE!"

181

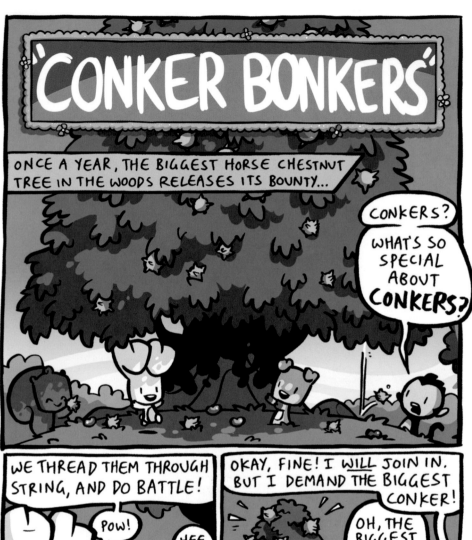

"CONKER BONKERS"

ONCE A YEAR, THE BIGGEST HORSE CHESTNUT TREE IN THE WOODS RELEASES ITS BOUNTY...

CONKERS?

WHAT'S SO SPECIAL ABOUT **CONKERS?**

WE THREAD THEM THROUGH STRING, AND DO BATTLE!

POW!

HEE HEE!

SMASH!

HMM...

OKAY, FINE! I WILL JOIN IN. BUT I DEMAND THE BIGGEST CONKER!

OH, THE BIGGEST ARE AT THE TOP OF THE TREE. NONE OF US CAN REACH THEM.

189

190

"ACTION PIG!"

NO, ACTION BEAVER CAN <u>NOT</u> COME OUT TO PLAY. HE SPENT ALL YESTERDAY JUMPING IN THE RIVER, AND NOW HE HAS A HIGH FEVER.

Bobble... Fft! Fft! Schhh...

ICE PACK

#1

AWW. WHO'S GOING TO TEST-DRIVE MY LATEST INVENTION, THE DRAGONFLY 5000, NOW?

BZZz!

HMMMM...

I WONDER.

O WHEEE! HA HA!

192

194

196

197

198

200

"DOOR B"

SKUNKY'S LAIR. HOME TO SOME OF THE MOST BIZARRE AND NIGHTMARISH CREATIONS YET TO WALK THE EARTH. A MYSTERIOUS CAVERN OF INVENTION AND DISCOVERY, SHROUDED IN SHADOW. FEW ENTER THIS PLACE, EVEN FEWER LEAVE.

WELCOME! (PLEASE GO AWAY)

ONLY CERTAIN SOULS WOULD EVER CONTEMPLATE VENTURING INSIDE...

THE BRAVE.

COME ON, WE DON'T HAVE LONG.

THE HUNGRY.

I BROUGHT A QUICHE FOR EMERGENCIES!

THE UNDENIABLY STUPID.

WHEN I WALK FAST, I KICK MYSELF IN THE FACE!

HEE HEE!

SOMETIMES, EVEN THE BRAVE, HUNGRY AND STUPID MUST WAIT FOR THEIR ANSWERS...

BECAUSE THE BIGGEST SECRETS ARE WELL PROTECTED.

AND THEY'RE THE ONES THAT ARE BEST LEFT UNKNOWN.

FOR NOW...

"HYPNO-MONKEY"

IT'S A RARE SUNNY DAY FOR THIS TIME OF YEAR, SO SKUNKY HAS DECIDED TO TAKE HIS WORK OUTSIDE...

HEY, SKUNKY, WHAT'S THIS? I FOUND IT. CAN I KICK IT?

HMM?

NO, MONKEY, PUT THAT DOWN. I AM CURRENTLY RESOLVING THE MOST COMPLICATED EQUATION KNOWN TO SCIENCE!

THE LAST THING I NEED IS YOU FIRING THAT AT ME.

WHY, WHAT IS IT?

IT IS A MEMORY RAY. IT RESETS THE BRAIN OF WHOEVER YOU FIRE IT AT!

SNATCH!

WIPES OUT THE MEMORIES.

'MONSTER PANTS!

IN THE DARKEST, SCARIEST CORNER OF THE WOODS, THREE INNOCENT FRIENDS TELL EACH OTHER THE MOST FRIGHTENING STORIES THEY KNOW...

AND THEN... I FELL OVER!

WOOOO.

WHAT, THAT'S IT? YOUR WHOLE STORY WAS THAT YOU FELL OVER? PIG, THAT'S NOT A SCARY STORY.

I LANDED ON MY NOSE.

HEE HEE. THAT'S A FUNNY STORY.

213

I'D HEARD RUMOURS OF MONSTER PANTS, OF COURSE. BUT NOTHING COULD PREPARE ME FOR WHAT I WAS TO MEET THAT NIGHT...

LA LA LA.

A GIANT PAIR OF PANTS, ALL ANGRY AND GNASHING ITS TEETH!

I WAS SCARED AND RAN AWAY.

BUT IT CHASED ME! ALL THROUGH THE WOODS, TRYING TO BITE MY TAIL OFF.

I ONLY ESCAPED BY HIDING IN MANURE.

WEENIE! THAT NEVER HAPPENED!

IT DID! IT DID HAPPEN!

IN FACT, EVEN TO THIS DAY...

...YOU CAN STILL HEAR MONSTER PANTS CHOMPING DOWN TREES!

WEENIE! YOUR PANTS! THEY'RE BALLOONING!

FWIPPP!

NO...

NO IT CAN'T BE...

215

216

218

"LOST IN THE SNOW!"

SNOW FALLS ON THE WOODS, COVERING EVERYTHING IN A GENTLE WHITE BLANKET...

...BUT WHAT IS THAT LYING UNDERNEATH?

AAAARGH! PLTHUH!

DID I DIE?

WHEN DID IT SNOW? I DON'T REMEMBER GETTING HERE. WHERE AM I? THAT WAS SOME PARTY.

DID I HAVE A PARTY?

ARGH! I'VE JUST BEEN WALKING AROUND IN A BIG CIRCLE!

HANG ON. I'M REMEMBERING MORE...

I STOMPED OUT INTO THE SNOW, IN A BIG SULK, TO GET AS FAR AWAY FROM BUNNY AS POSSIBLE.

WHEN SUDDENLY...

BONK!

NYAHH!

...A LOG KNOCKED ME OUT!

IT WAS YOU. YOU LEFT ME OUT HERE IN THE FIRST PLACE.

I CHEWED YOUR FEET FOR A BIT, BUT THEY TASTED LIKE OLD BANANAS.

HEE HEE, LOOK! MISTER MONKEY AND MISTER FOX ARE PLAYING IN THE SNOW!

RRGHH!

WHO'S MONKEY?

"CHEMICAL X!"

WOOSH WOOSH, THROUGH THE SNOW, A SLEDGING PIG IS ON THE GO...

LUCKY HE LOVES PLAYING IN IT, BECAUSE HE'LL FALL OFF ANY MINUTE...

THUNK!

SHRIEK!

NO! YOU STAY AWAY FROM THIS, PIG! IT IS NOT FOR YOU! NO!

NO!

NOPE.

EE HEE HEE!

227

228

A YEAR FROM NOW, THE WOODS ARE RULED BY A **MONKEY!** HE DESTROYS EVERYTHING, ENSLAVES US ALL, AND TURNS LIFE INTO A **NIGHTMARE!!**

WHAT? DON'T BE SO SILLY. IF ANYONE WAS TO TAKE OVER, IT WOULD BE ME! I'M A GENIUS!

NOT IF HE GETS HIS HANDS ON YOUR TOP SECRET **DOOMSDAY DEVICE!**

GASP! HOW DID YOU KNOW ABOUT THAT?

I'M YOU. SHEESH! I'M NOT AS CLEVER AS I REMEMBER.

IN APPROXIMATELY ONE MINUTE, YOU ARE GOING TO MEET THIS MONKEY FOR THE FIRST TIME. YOU'LL SHOW HIM YOUR LABORATORY, WHERE HE'LL SEIZE CONTROL OF THE DOOMSDAY DEVICE!

USING IT TO TAKE OVER THE WOODS!

SO, IT IS IMPERATIVE THAT YOU NEVER SHOW HIM THE DEVICE. SHOW HIM EVERYTHING ELSE, IMPRESS HIM WITH YOUR CREATIONS.

TAKE HIM FOR A RIDE ON THE **CLUCK CLUCK ZEPPELIN** IF YOU WANT.

JUST NEVER EVER SHOW HIM THE DOOMSDAY DEVICE!

232

RIGHT! OKAY! WHATEVER THAT IS, I'LL STOP HIM DISCOVERING IT.

QUICKLY! HE WON'T STOP FIRING WATERMELONS!

PTOO!

BWOOP!!

FOUR MONTHS AGO...

OH CRIPES, IS IT SUMMER ALREADY?

BEHOLD! I FOUND THIS AT THE BACK OF MY LAIR. THE DOOMSDAY DEVICE!

IT WILL DESTROY EVERYTHING OF BEAUTY, ANNIHILATE ALL HAPPINESS, AND BRING MISERY TO THE WOODS!

ARGH! I'M TOO LATE!

FUTURE ME WAS LEFT IN THE PAST AND FORGOT TO NOT SHOW MONKEY THE THING HE COULDN'T REMEMBER ANYWAY!

AND NOW PAST ME, WHICH IS ME, ARRIVED FROM THE FUTURE TO SEE FUTURE ME DO IT! IN THE PAST!

I THINK.

BUT I ONLY HAVE SECONDS LEFT HERE. HOW CAN I UNDO EVENTS AND SAVE THE FUTURE?

235

"MERRY CHRISTMAS MISTER MONKEY!"

HAVE YOU TWO SEEN MONKEY?

NOPE! WE'VE BEEN HERE ALL NIGHT, DECORATING THE TREES WITH JELLY!

HAPPY CHRISTMAS

IT'S NOT JUST TONIGHT. I HAVEN'T SEEN HIM AROUND FOR THE LAST COUPLE OF WEEKS!

HE'S UP TO SOMETHING.

MAYBE YOU COULD ASK... HUBBUB UBBUBBB!

PIG? ARE YOU OKAY?

HUBBUBB UBBUBB! UBB! UBB!

UBBB!

HE'LL BE FINE. SOMETIMES HE REMEMBERS IT'S CHRISTMAS TOMORROW, AND HIS BRAIN FUSES WITH ALL THE EXCITEMENT!

GIVE IT 3... 2... 1...

...UBBUBB...LE FOX, MAYBE HE'S SEEN MONKEY?

UMMM.

OKAY SURE, THANKS, PIG.

LE FOX? I DIDN'T EXPECT YOU TO GET INTO THE FESTIVE SPIRIT.

ZIS WAS NOT MY CHOICE. THAT STUPID SQUIRREL BRIBED ME WITH HIS DELICIOUS MINCE PIES.

HE PUTS A CHERRY ON TOP.

BUT IF ANYONE COMES NEAR ME, ASKING FOR PRESENTS, I'LL BITE THEM ON THE **BUMS.**

CHOMP!

OHHH-KAYY. LE FOX, HAVE YOU SEEN MONKEY?

HMM, NOT SINCE I BURIED HIM IN THE SNOW A WHILE AGO.

HE'S PROBABLY STILL LOST...

LOST? THAT'S TERRIBLE!

WHY DO YOU CARE? IT IS **MONKEY.** NONE OF US ACTUALLY LIKE HIM.

BUT... IT'S **CHRISTMAS!**

I SHALL <u>FIND</u> MONKEY, AND SHOW HIM WHAT IT MEANS TO BE GOOD TO EACH OTHER AT THIS SPECIAL TIME OF YEAR.

PERHAPS I CAN HELP. I'VE FOUND MONKEY'S ABSENCE SUSPICIOUS TOO. FORTUNATELY FOR US ALL, THE TRACKING DEVICE I IMPLANTED IN HIS SKULL WILL LEAD US RIGHT TO HIM!

EXCEPT... HE'S NOT SHOWING UP ON MY SCREEN. HE MUST BE OUT OF RANGE!

NOTHING

MONKEY TRACKER

240

241

242

243

THIS IS WHAT I THOUGHT HUMANS LOOK LIKE. BIG, WEIRD, UGLY THINGS, THAT WE WOODLAND ANIMALS SHOULDN'T GO NEAR.

LOOK, THIS IS NEW FOR ALL OF US, BUT NOW WE HAVE DISCOVERED HUMANS EXIST, WE MUST BE CAREFUL NOT TO EXAGGERATE THINGS.

WE NEED TO ESTABLISH SOME FACTS.

FACTS? YOU WANT FACTS?

HERE'S A FACT. AVOID HUMANS.

I'M SCARED JUST BEING ONE!

WHAT DO YOU KNOW ABOUT HUMANS, SKUNKY? IT WAS YOU WHO RECOGNISED THEM AFTER ALL!

ME? OH, UH... NOTHING.

NOTHING AT ALL.

AHEM.

HE LIES! HE IS IN LEAGUE WITH THE HUMANS.

OH YEAH? WANNA TAKE THIS OUTSIDE, FOX?

HOW TO DRAW BUNNY

①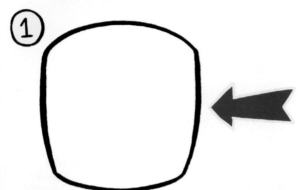

FIRST, LET'S DRAW **THE HEAD!** BUNNY'S HEAD LOOKS LIKE A **BULGING SQUARE!**

②

ADD AN **EAR!** TRY DRAWING A **HEART SHAPE** FOR BUNNY'S EAR.

③

ADD **ANOTHER EAR!** DRAW A SECOND HEART TUCKED BEHIND THE FIRST.

248

NOW... BUNNY'S FACE!

① TRY DRAWING A CROSS -THIS WILL HELP YOU TO WORK OUT WHERE BUNNY'S FACE FITS ON HIS HEAD!

② FOR INSTANCE, HIS **EYES** SIT ON THE HORIZONTAL LINE!

③ ABOVE HIS EYES, ADD TWO CURVED LINES FOR **EYEBROWS!**

④ A LITTLE TRIANGLE FOR A **NOSE...**

⑤ ANOTHER CURVED LINE FOR A **SMILING MOUTH...**

⑥ AND FINALLY A LITTLE TUFT OF **CHEEK HAIR!**

AND THEN... THE BODY!

ALL THE CHARACTERS IN BUNNY VS MONKEY HAVE A **LUMP** FOR A BODY. IT MIGHT HELP TO IMAGINE IT LIKE A **CURVED TRIANGLE**, OR EVEN A **SHARK'S FIN!**

① WE THEN ADD A CIRCULAR PATCH OF **TUMMY FUR**...

② A SAUSAGE SHAPE FOR HIS **ARM**...

③ ANOTHER SAUSAGE FOR THE **OTHER ARM.** (TRY ADDING FINGERS TO THE END OF IT!)

④ A BOBBLE TAIL!

⑤ AND THAT'S **BUNNY!**

THESE ARE THE BASIC STEPS FOR DRAWING BUNNY. ONCE YOU'VE MASTERED THESE, IT'S IMPORTANT TO KEEP PRACTISING! IT WILL BECOME EASIER AND EASIER, AND THE BUNNIES YOU DRAW WILL LOOK MORE AND MORE NATURAL! TRY GIVING HIM DIFFERENT POSES, TOO! DIFFERENT EXPRESSIONS! STRETCH HIS FIGURE OUT AND SEE WHAT YOU CAN MAKE HIM DO!

NOTICE THE **FEET** ON THIS BUNNY – JUST TWO LITTLE CIRCLES!

⚡ HOW TO DRAW ⚡ MONKEY

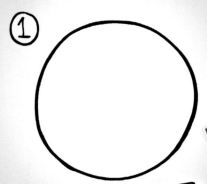

1

MONKEY'S HEAD STARTS WITH A **GREAT BIG CIRCLE!**

2

ADD A TRIANGLE AT THE TOP. THIS IS THE **PEAK** OF HIS FUR!

3

THEN A SQUARE FOR THE FIRST TUFT...

4

ANOTHER FOR THE SECOND TUFT...

5

ONE MORE TRIANGLE ON THE SIDE...

6

AND THEN MONKEY'S **EAR** NEXT TO IT. HIS EARS ARE **EGG-SHAPED**, WITH A LITTLE 'T' SQUIGGLED INSIDE!

7

ADD A LITTLE DARK LUMP FOR THE EAR ON THE OTHER SIDE!

AND NOW FOR MONKEY'S FACE!

1 TRY DRAWING THE CROSS ON MONKEY'S FACE TOO...

2 IT WILL HELP YOU FIND WHERE TO DRAW HIS **EYES!**

3 ADD TWO CURVED TRIANGLES FOR HIS **EYEBROWS.**

4 HIS **MOUTH** HERE IS JUST A STRAIGHT LINE, WITH A ROW OF **TEETH** POKING OUT!

5 AND THEN, OF COURSE, THERE'S HIS **NOSE.**

WHY NOT TRY **COPYING** SOME OF THESE **DIFFERENT EXPRESSIONS?**

GRUMPY

HAPPY

CONFUSED

ANGRY

FINALLY... MONKEY'S BODY!

(1) MONKEY'S BODY IS THE SAME LUMP WE DREW FOR BUNNY...

(2) ... WITH THE SAME CIRCLE FOR HIS BELLY!

(3) HE, TOO, HAS SAUSAGES FOR ARMS... BUT REMEMBER TO DRAW IN THE SLEEVE WHERE HIS FUR ENDS!

FINGERS + THUMB! → ← FUR ENDS

(4) ADD ANOTHER ARM ON THE OTHER SIDE!

(5) DON'T FORGET HIS TWISTY TAIL!

(6) AND THAT'S MONKEY!

AND AGAIN, IF YOU KEEP DRAWING MONKEY HE'LL LOOK BETTER AND BETTER! TRY DIFFERENT EXPRESSIONS AND POSES! DRAW HIM CAUSING RIDICULOUS TROUBLE!

JAMIE SMART HAS BEEN CREATING CHILDREN'S COMICS FOR MANY YEARS, WITH POPULAR TITLES INCLUDING *BUNNY VS MONKEY*, *LOOSHKIN*, AND *FISH-HEAD STEVE*, WHICH BECAME THE FIRST WORK OF ITS SORT TO BE SHORTLISTED FOR THE ROALD DAHL FUNNY PRIZE. THE FIRST IN HIS SERIES OF ILLUSTRATED NOVELS, *FLEMBER: THE SECRET BOOK*, IS AVAILABLE NOW. HE ALSO WORKS ON MULTIMEDIA PROJECTS LIKE *FIND CHAFFY*.

JAMIE LIVES IN THE SOUTH-EAST OF ENGLAND, WHERE HE SPENDS HIS TIME THINKING UP STORIES AND GETTING LOST ON DOG WALKS.